ARMOR SERIES   VOL. 5

STRASSEN PANZER

by
Walter J. Spielberger
and
Uwe Feist

Aero Publishers, Inc.

FALLBROOK, CALIFORNIA

We wish to acknowledge our appreciation to the following who
have provided photographs for this volume:
Bibliothek für Zeitgeschichte, Stuttgart.
National Archive and Record Service.
Colonel Robert J. Icks.
A. J. North of Warpics.
H. J. Nowarra.
Peter Chamberlain

Editor's note: Because the original German specifications and terms used in this book are based on the metric system, the following table is included for convenient referral.

unit	abbreviation	approximate U.S. equivalent
1 centimeter	cm	0.39 inches
1 kilogram	kg	2.2046 pounds
1 kilopond	kp	2.2046 pounds (not affected by atmospheric pressure)
1 kilometer	km	0.62 miles
1 liter	ltr	1.057 quarts liquid
1 metric ton	t	1.1 tons
1 millimeter	mm	0.04 inches

Printed and Published in the United States of America by Aero Publishers, Inc.

STRASSENPANZER

by

Walter J. Spielberger

After World War I, Germany was not permitted, under the Treaty of Versailles, to possess either tanks or armored cars except a limited number of armored personnel carriers to be used by Police.

The lack of armored vehicles during the late Twenties forced the German Army High Command to create dummy tanks which could be used during maneuvers and field exercises in the place of tanks. As early as in 1925, dummy tanks were issued to troops. At this time, however, they consisted only of frames made of steel tubes and covered with canvas, simulating tanks. These contraptions were not motorized, were mounted on three rubber wheels and had to be pushed by two men. The first dummy armored car mounted on a truck chassis appeared in 1928, the design coming from the Kf. 6 in Hannover, and immediately following a second dummy armored car was issued to troops. All the truck chassis built by the company of Büssing-NAG were road-bound. It proved, therefore, necessary to fall back on a passenger car chassis for the further development of dummy tanks. By 1929, dummy tank hulls were mounted on the chassis of the light passenger car BMW/Dixi Type 3/15. These vehicles were replaced in 1930 by a tank imitation mounted on an Adler chassis. This Adler chassis had a four-man crew and was equipped with a rotating turret. This chassis was later used for light armored cars Kfz. 13 and 14.

Even after the renunciation of the Treaty of Versailles, the German Army could not forego using this inexpensive and efficient means of training. Therefore, from 1935 on, a dummy tank hull based on the chassis of the domestic light passenger car was put into use. Exclusively used for this purpose was the Opel chassis Type "1936", which was equipped with an Opel 1.3 litre 4-cylinder gasoline engine with 28.5 hp. With a two-man crew, the armament consisted of one MG 34 in a rotating turret. After this chassis was taken off production, the Volkswagen chassis, Type "82", was supposed to take its place.

Armored personnel carriers

The armored personnel police cars built by the companies of Daimler-Benz and Ehrhardt, allowed by the Treaty of Versailles, in no way represented the tactical ideas of the Army Ministry. This forced the Ordnance Department in 1926/27, to secretly issue design specifications for 8 and/or 10 wheeled chassis for armored personnel carriers.

The Ordnance Department of the Army Ministry placed orders for this type of vehicle with the companies of C. D. Magirus in Ulm, Büssing-NAG in Braunschweig, and Daimler-Benz in Stuttgart-Untertürkheim. Each one of these companies had built prototypes by 1929 which were thoroughly tested in both Kummersdorf and Wünsdorf.

It is interesting to note that while the companies of Magirus and Daimler-Benz worked with 8-wheeled vehicles, the company of Büssing-NAG developed a 10-wheeled one. The planning for the Daimler-Benz types was done in the central design office of this company in Stuttgart-Untertürkheim, under the supervision of Prof. F. Porsche. Components for both prototypes were also built in Stuttgart, but the final assembly took place in the Daimler-Benz factory in Berlin-Marienfelde.

Responsible for the unitized bodies was the company Martini & Hüneke in Salzkotten, while the turret and the weapon came from the Rheinmetall Company in Düsseldorf. To camouflage the whole endeavor, the armored bodies were enclosed in a cork body which was also supposed to increase the floating ability of the vehicle. The rear steering mechanism was so designed that the steering columns and the hand and foot pedals of the rear driver seat could be removed. This was mainly done to divert the attention of the Inter-Allied Control Office for Germany. After extensive trials, the Reichswehr took over the first vehicles by the end of 1930 and the beginning of 1931. Parts of these vehicles were also sent for further trial runs to the German maintained Ordnance Research Institute in Kazan, Russia. Because of the impaired economic situation in Germany during the years of 1929 and 1930, mass production of special vehicles of this kind could not be materialized, neither was it possible to incorporate the given technical advancements in vehicles for domestic use.

A discussion with an official of the Ordnance Department on March 18, 1930, came to the following conclusion: "The purchase of vehicles of this kind is out of the question because of the present financial situation of the Reich."

Heavy armored cars (six-wheeled)

By June of 1929, the War Ministry/Ordnance Branch had issued specifications for the delivery of 6×4 trucks for military purposes. Here, again, the companies of C. D. Magirus, Büssing-NAG and Daimler-Benz were prominently engaged. As a result, C. D. Magirus developed the type "M-206", Büssing-NAG the type "G-31", while Daimler-Benz AG already had built the type "G-3" in 1928, which was replaced by the modified type "G-3a" in 1929.

Pre-trials with a Daimler-Benz chassis of the type "G-3" which was at this time at the disposal of the Ordnance Department, revealed that these chassis eventually could be used in connection with armored bodies. With a chassis weight of 2200 kp and body weight of 2300 kp, the total permissable weight came to 4½ tons. It was felt, however, that it was necessary to reinforce the front axle, and also to increase the cooling area of the radiator. The chassis, which were intended for use in connection with armored bodies, again used dual steering (front and rear), and all these aforementioned improvements were incorporated in all future deliveries of 6×4 chassis. Also investigated was the use of larger tires to increase cross-country ability. By 1932, the Ordnance Department had ordered 37 Daimler-Benz chassis type "G-3a", while Büssing-NAG had 12 chassis for armored cars under construction, while the total order was for 50 units.

The armored bodies for these vehicles were almost exclusively manufactured by the Deutsche Werke AG in Kiel, the total permissable weight now being approximately 5000 kp.

General Heinz Guderian indicates in his book "Panzer Leader", the first official use of these armored cars: "...during the maneuvers of the year 1932 for the first time German armored cars of an interim design, mounted on the chassis of a 6×4 truck, appeared..."

The technical layout followed conventional lines; three rigid axles were mounted on a straight frame by means of leaf springs. The two rear axles with dual tires were driven. The Daimler-Benz used a 6-cylinder gasoline engine, type "M 09", with 68 hp; Büssing-NAG used a 4-cylinder gasoline engine, type "G", with 65 hp; and the C. D. Magirus AG used a 6-cylinder gasoline engine, type "S 88", with 70 hp output.

With improved bodies and other refinements, these vehicles were issued to troops after 1933, and provided the backbone for the German armored reconnaissance units. The official nomenclature was as follows:

a) Schwere Panzerspähwagen (6-Rad) (Sd. Kfz. 231)
Heavy armored reconnaissance car (6-wheeled)

b) Schwere Panzerspähwagen (Fu) (Sd. Kfz. 232)
Heavy armored reconnaissance car (radio)

c) Panzerfunkwagen (Sd. Kfz. 263)
Armored communication car

While Sd. Kfz. 231 and 233 were equipped with a 2 cm gun and a MG 13 in a rotating turret, the Sd. Kfz. 263 only had one MG 13 in a rigid mount. The large antennae for both Sd. Kfz. 263 and 232 characterized radio vehicles of that time. Armor averaged 14.5 mm. Manufacturers for the armored hulls were the Deutschen Werke AG in Kiel and the Deutsche Edelstahlwerke AG in Hannover-Linden.

These vehicles were only supposed to be an interim solution until the heavy armored reconnaissance car on the 8-wheeled chassis was available. They had to be used, however, during early wartime actions in Poland and France. After that, they were only used for training purposes.

Machine gun carriers and radio vehicles with medium domestic passenger car chassis

To supplement the reconnaissance units with lighter and more flexible vehicles, the Ordnance Department decided to equip domestic passenger car chassis with light armored bodies. Daimler-Benz AG in Berlin-Marienfelde was responsible for this development, while the armored hulls came mainly from the Deutsche Edelstahl AG in Hannover-Linden. These hulls were exclusively mounted on Adler chassis. They had an open top and received the following nomenclature:

a) Maschinengewehrkraftwagen (Kfz. 13)
   Machine gun carrier

b) Funkkraftwagen (Kfz. 14)
   Radio car

The weak armor of 8 mm did not allow an extensive combat use of these vehicles. Also, the cross-country ability of these domestic passenger car chassis left much to be desired. Armament for the two-man Kfz. 13 was an MG 13, while Kfz. 14 had a three-man crew without armament. For training purposes, however, these vehicles established a good reputation with the cavalry regiments and the heavy companies of the reconnaissance battalions of the infantry divisions. They were gradually replaced by a light armored car on the standard chassis during the years of 1937 and 1938. The Kfz. 13 and 14 saw front service in Poland in 1939 and were later exclusively used as training vehicles.

Light armored reconnaissance cars with standard chassis I for heavy passenger cars

As a by-product of the standard chassis I for heavy passenger cars, a chassis with a rear engine for light armored cars was built after 1935 as a replacement for the Kfz. 13 and 14. Responsible for this development was Eisenwerk Weserhütte AG in Bad Oeynhausen, while the chassis were built at the Horchwerke of the Auto-Union AG in Zwickau. Final assembly took place also at the plants of F. Schichau in Elbing and the Maschinenfabrik Niedersachsen in Hannover-Linden. As with all the other standard chassis for passenger cars and light trucks, developed by the Ordnance Department, these vehicles had coil springs in triangular mounts. This independent wheel arrangement, together with four-wheel drive and four-wheel steering established adequate cross-country ability. A Horch V-8 gasoline engine of approximately 3.5 ltr. displacement and an output of 75 hp allowed the 4.8 ton vehicle a top speed of 80 km per hour. Built from 1935 to 1939, this was the A-version of the vehicle with mechanical brakes. Starting in June of 1940, the B-version appeared, having the 3.8 ltr. Horch engine with 90 hp installed and using a hydraulic brake system. Officially used by troops were, starting in 1935, the following vehicles:

a) Leichter Panzerspähwagen (MG) (Sd. Kfz. 221)
   Light armored reconnaissance car

b) Leichter Panzerspähwagen (Sd. Kfz. 221) mit 2.8 cm s PzB 41
   Light armored reconnaissance car with 2.8 cm heavy anti-tank rifle 41

c) Leichter Panzerspähwagen (2 cm) (Sd. Kfz. 222)
   Light armored reconnaissance car (2 cm)

d) Leichter Panzerspähwagen (Fu) (Sd. Kfz. 223)
   Light armored reconnaissance car (Radio)

e) Kleiner Panzerfunkwagen (Sd. Kfz. 261)
   Small armored radio car

f) Kleiner Panzerfunkwagen (Sd. Kfz. 260)
   Small armored radio car

The total weight of these vehicles was between 4 and 4.8 tons, the chassis weight was 1965 kp. Average production time was approximately 12 months.

A new order was placed by the Ordnance Department on April 20, 1940, with Appel in Berlin-Spandau and Schichau in Elbing, for the installation of a 2 cm anti-aircraft gun arrangement for the Sd. Kfz. 222. It was intended to use this vehicle also for anti-aircraft purposes. The total weight, however, rose to 5000 kp.

The armored hulls had plates of 10—14.5 mm while the hull fronts were sometimes increased up to 30 mm. The crew consisted of two men on Sd. Kfz. 221, three men on Sd. Kfz. 222/223 and four men on Sd. Kfz. 260/261. Despite the fact that the production of these vehicles stopped in 1942, some were still in use with the German armed forces until the end of the war.

Once again, improvements were contemplated for the light armored reconnaissance car (4-wheeled) in 1941. An order went to the Ordnance Department on July 21, 1941, to develop a chassis which was similar to the 8-wheeled "Tp" armored car. In utilizing many parts of this larger vehicle, the new 4-wheeled vehicle was similar with the exception of engine, transmission, suspension system, and shortened hull. The air-cooled 6-cylinder Tatra Diesel engine with an output of 125 hp was supposed to give the 7-ton vehicle a top speed of 85 km an hour. Front armor was 30 mm, while the rest was between 8 and 14.5 mm. Büssing-NAG in Berlin-Oberschöneweide was responsible for the design of the chassis. Subsequent production of the chassis was entrusted to the Horchwerke in Zwickau. The crew consisted of four men; armament was a 2 cm gun 39/1 and a MG 42 in a rotating turret.

1000 vehicles were ordered with an intended start of mass production in October, 1943. War conditions, however, made this impossible.

Heavy armored reconnaissance car with 8-wheeled standard chassis

Falling back on experiences gained with the 8- and/or 10-wheeled vehicles of the years 1927 through 1930, and combined with additional experience gained with the standard vehicles of the German Army, the chassis type "GS" was developed during 1934—1935 by Büssing-NAG in Leipzig-Wahren. This chassis again had independent wheel suspension and was equipped with 8-wheel drive and 8-wheel steering. On the rear end of a very sturdy frame, a Büssing 8-cylinder "Vee" gasoline engine, type "L 8 V" was installed, while two steering mechanisms for forward and reverse driving completed this special chassis. The chassis weight was 4120 kp. Originally with an output of 150 hp, this performance was increased to 180 hp by means of enlarging the bore, allowing a top speed of almost 100 km an hour. Total weight of the vehicle was 8.5 tons. Deutsche Werke AG in Kiel was responsible for the development of this armored vehicle, while assembly took place also at the plant of F. Schichau in Elbing. These vehicles represented the heavy standard equipment of the armored reconnaissance units until the end of the war. A total of 1235 units were produced. Officially issued to troops were the following different units:

a) Schwerer Panzerspähwagen (Sd. Kfz. 231) (8-Rad)
   Heavy armored reconnaissance car (Sd. Kfz. 231) (8-wheeled)

b) Schwerer Panzerspähwagen (Sd. Kfz. 232) (Fu) (8-Rad)
   Heavy armored reconnaissance car (Sd. Kfz. 232) (Radio) (8-wheeled)

c) Schwerer Panzerspähwagen (7,5 cm) (Sd. Kfz. 233)
   Heavy armored reconnaissance car (7.5 cm) (Sd. Kfz. 233)

d) Panzerfunkwagen (Sd. Kfz. 263) (8-Rad)
   Armored Radio Car (Sd. Kfz. 263) (8-wheeled)

The basic armor of all the vehicles was between 10—14.5 mm. The hull front, however, was in most cases increased to 30 mm. The average construction time was 12 months. Sd. Kfz. 231 and 232 had a 4-man crew, armament consisted of a 2 cm KwK 30 and/or 38, and a MG 34 in a rotating turret. The somewhat cumbersome original antennae of the radio vehicles Sd. Kfz. 232 and 263 were replaced by a single pole antenna, starting in 1942. Sd. Kfz. 233 and 263 had rigid turrets. While vehicle 233, which was used as a support vehicle, mounted a 7.5 cm tank gun L/24, armament of the Sd. Kfz. 263 consisted of only one MG 34. This vehicle, however, had a 5-man crew. Assembly of this vehicle was exclusively done at the Deutsche Werke in Kiel.

Vehicles of these series were partly equipped during the war years with an additional armor plate, which was hinged to the front of the vehicle. After 1938, these armored cars with an 8-wheeled standard chassis replaced the heavy 6-wheeled types. Production of the Pz. FuWg. Sd. Kfz. 263 ceased in January, 1942. This production capacity was taken over by the medium half-tracked armored personnel carriers, series 251. Construction of the other 8-wheeled standard units stopped during the year 1942. The production of the "L 8 V" motor continued until 1944.

Heavy armored reconnaissance car for tropical areas (8-wheeled)

While the production of the 8-wheeled standard chassis was still in full swing, a new order was received by the Ordnance Department on August 5, 1940, for the construction of an 8-wheeled armored car similar to the standard chassis which, however, was to be equipped with a unitized body instead of a frame. This order was issued to the company of Tatra in Nesselsdorf for the development of a 12-cylinder air-cooled Diesel engine with approximately 200 hp output. This engine was supposed to be ready for production by the end of 1941. Büssing-NAG in Berlin-Oberschöneweide was responsible for the development of the unitized body, while the companies of Daimler-Benz and F. Schichau were made responsible for the turret. The total weight was supposed to be between 10.5 and 11.5 tons, the front armor to be 30 mm, the rest of the vehicle between 8—14.5 mm. Intended top speed was 85 km an hour. Mounted in a rotating turret were a 5 cm KwK 39/1 and a MG 42. The crew consisted of four men. The first prototype was delivered in July 1942. Constant improvements and changes were necessary on the first Diesel engine, especially because of the above average noise level. The third engine, which was supposed to be fit for tropical use, was planned to be delivered by June, 1942. This development, however, was later cancelled. The vehicle went into mass production in July 1943, and appeared in following models:

a) Schwerer Panzerspähwagen (Sd. Kfz. 234/1)
   Heavy armored reconnaissance car (Sd. Kfz. 234/1)

b) Schwerer Panzerspähwagen 5 cm (Sd. Kfz. 234/2)
   Heavy armored reconnaissance car 5 cm (Sd. Kfz. 234/2)

c) Schwerer Panzerspähwagen 7.5 cm (Sd. Kfz. 234/3)
   Heavy armored reconnaissance car 7.5 cm (Sd. Kfz. 234/3)

d) Schwerer Panzerspähwagen 7.5 cm (Sd. Kfz. 234/4)
   Heavy armored reconnaissance car 7.5 cm (Sd. Kfz. 234/4)

The Sd. Kfz. 234/4 mounted the entire upper mount with barrel and shield of the 7.5 cm wheeled Pak 40 in the middle of the fighting compartment. This installation was done on Hitler's personal order.

While the chassis were built and the assembly took place at the Büssing-NAG in Leipzig, the armored bodies came from the Deutsche Edelstahlwerke in Krefeld. Armor plates for hull and turret were 30 mm thick in front, while the side plates were 8 mm; rear armor was 10 mm. With the Diesel engine and the enlarged tires (270—20), the cruising range was almost 1000 km and increased immensely the combat ability of these vehicles. From 1944 on, the armored cars of the 234 series replaced vehicles of the former 8-wheeled series and represented with their most modern construction details some of the most advanced armored vehicles of the Second World War. A total of approximately 2300 units were completed.

Heavy armored cross-country passenger cars

In order to complete the armored wheeled vehicles of the German Army, it is necessary to mention those which were issued under the nomenclature "Sd. Kfz. 247". These vehicles were originally mounted on the chassis of the domestic light cross-country truck: (Krupp Type "L 2 H 43 and 143"). From 1938 on, the standard chassis II for heavy passenger cars was used. The Daimler-Benz factory in Marienfelde was responsible for the development of these vehicles while the armored bodies were mainly obtained from the Deutsche Edelstahl Werke in Hannover-Linden. Vehicles of this kind were used principally by high-ranking staff officers and were issued to units in limited numbers only.

"Schildkröte" (turtle) — series of the Trippelwerke in Molsheim/ Alsace

Based on the amphibious passenger car type "SG 6" of the Trippel Company, three prototypes of a light amphibious armored car were developed from 1941 through October of 1942. While "Schildkröte I" was equipped with one machine gun, "Schildkröte II" was supposed to receive one 20 mm heavy machine gun 151 and/or two MGs. The third prototype "Schildkröte III" was supposed to carry only one 20 mm heavy machine gun 151. Originally planned with an armor of 7—7.5 mm, this was later increased to 10 mm. These vehicles were equipped with air-cooled Tatra V 8 gasoline engine and were not too successful. Development was halted by the end of 1944.

Armored vehicles taken over from other armies

Only very few of the captured vehicles taken over by the German Army were used by German units. One was the vehicle "RR 7" of the Austrian Saurerwerke AG, which was issued to German reconnaissance units as the Sd. Kfz. 254. The design of this vehicle dates back to 1930 when the Austrian Automotive Industry in close connection with the Ordnance Department of the Austrian Army developed cross-country vehicles. At that time, the Saurerwerke developed the type "RR", a wheel-cum-track vehicle which was able to use wheels on roads and tracks off the roads. The change from wheels to tracks could be done while the vehicle was in motion. These vehicles were equipped with a Saurer 4-cylinder Diesel engine and were supposed to be used as light artillery tractors and as a chassis for light tanks. The RR chassis, which originally had solid rubber tires, received pneumatic tires and was re-named "RR 7". An order for 15 of these units was placed after extensive trial runs in January, 1937. The annexation of Austria in 1938 did not interrupt this development because on the 21st of May, 1938, an order was placed by the German Ordnance Department with the Saurerwerke in Vienna, to develop an armored reconnaissance vehicle for wheel and track driving with radio equipment. While Saurerwerke was responsible for both chassis and body, the Daimler-Benz factory in Berlin designed the turret. The suggested delivery of the first vehicle was supposed to be around the end of May, 1942. Nomenclature for this vehicle was "Panzerspähwagen RK (Ausführung A)" — Armored Reconnaissance car RK (Model A) —, the total weight was 6.5 tons. Armor plates varied from 5.5 to 14.5 mm. It was powered by a Saurer Diesel engine with 100 hp output. Armament constisted of a MG 34 in a rotating turret, the crew of three men. This vehicle, however, never reached the production stage, only the above-mentioned Sd. Kfz. 254 was available to troops in very limited numbers. A total of 140 units was anticipated and completed by November, 1940. A sideline of this vehicle was the Instandsetzungskraftwagen (Maintenance vehicle), with a payload of 1500 kp which used the same chassis. An improved prototype, type "RK 9", was tested during 1940 and 1941. Despite the fact that the Waffen-SS was most interested in this vehicle, mass production was never started.

Wheel-armored cars for export purposes

Despite the tense economic situation during the re-arming phase of the German Army, it was found impossible to forego the income deriving from export sales. Because of the interest of several nations in German armament products, some armored vehicles were exported. The company of Friedrich Krupp principally was involved in these contracts and delivered a number of armored vehicles, based on a 6×4 chassis of the type "L 2 H 43 and 143" to the Dutch East Indies.

The original Daimler chassis, used for armored police cars had dual steering and was based on the well-known Krupp-Daimler artillery tractor used in substantial numbers during World War I.

The light armor afforded protection against small arm fire and allowed the vehicles to be used successfully during internal riots in post-war Germany.

Gepanzerter Kraftwagen (Sd. Kfz. 3)

CREW	6		
COMBAT WEIGHT	12000 kp		
LENGTH	5950 mm		
WIDTH	2200 mm		
HEIGHT	2725 mm		
MAXIMUM SPEED	50 km/h		
MAXIMUM RANGE	300 km		
ARMAMENT	2 heavy MG		
AMMUNITION			
ARMOR	FRONT	10 mm	
	SIDE	7.5 mm	
	TOP	7.5 mm	
	REAR	7.5 mm	
ENGINE	Daimler "M 1574" 4, inline, gasoline 100 HP		
TRANSMISSION	FORWARD 5	REVERSE 5	
FUEL CAPACITY	250 ltr.		
TRACK WIDTH	—		
MANUFACTURER	Daimler-Motoren-Gesellschaft, Stuttgart		
NUMBER MANUFACTURED	31		

The chassis again had dual controls, making it more flexible for street fighting conditions within crowded city streets.

Despite their 4-wheel drive, these units were mainly street-bound and possessed almost no cross-country ability. The hub-like protrusion on the front wheels served to give the vehicle more traction in deep sand.

The police version of the "DZVR" had two rotating machine gun turrets and an observation tower in the center. These vehicles were also taken over later by the Army.

This is the unit as used by the Reichswehr as an armored personnel carrier. It carried no turret.

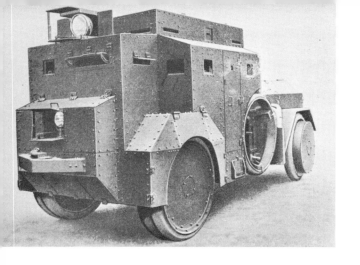

A rear view of the military version shows observation ports and details of the rivetted armor.

The Benz version built also in 1921 was similar to the Daimler vehicle and was used almost exclusively for police purposes.

Its chassis had the usual dual controls and 4-wheel drive. Because of its weight, it was mainly street-bound.

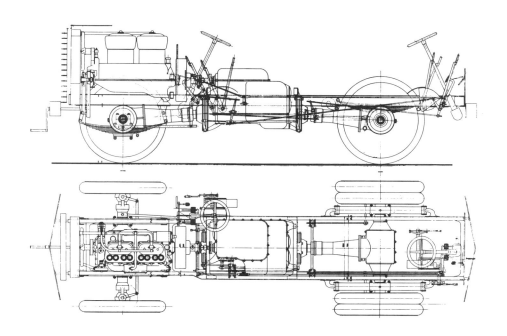

This is the Ehrhard version of the police armored car, with a super-structure similar to the one of the Daimler and the Benz. All these armored bodies were produced by Martini & Hüneke of Salzkotten.

The 8-wheeled armored car developed by Daimler-Benz AG. in secrecy was a very modern vehicle for its time. Here it is shown being unloaded from a trailer during initial trials in 1930.

Camouflaged with a cork body which also helped the amphibious ability of the unit and showing a crew for water propulsion mounted on the front of the vehicle, this unit underwent extensive trials both in Germany and Russia.

A wooden model of the unit shows the ballistically well shaped hull and the proposed turret, which was never completed.

Mannschafts-Transportwagen I

CREW	5	
COMBAT WEIGHT	7800 kp	
LENGTH	5450 mm	
WIDTH	2280 mm	
HEIGHT	2135 mm	
MAXIMUM SPEED	65 km/h	
MAXIMUM RANGE	250 km	
ARMAMENT	1 3.7 cm tank gun	
AMMUNITION	66 rounds	
ARMOR	FRONT	13.5 mm
	SIDE	13.5 mm
	TOP	—
	REAR	13.5 mm
ENGINE	Daimler-Benz "M 36" 6 cyl inline, gasoline	
TRANSMISSION	FORWARD 5	REVERSE 5
FUEL CAPACITY	170 ltr.	
TRACK WIDTH	—	
MANUFACTURER	Daimler-Benz AG., Marienfelde	
NUMBER MANUFACTURED	2	

This is the unit without the cork body, showing the unitized armored frame-body assembly. These units were highly mobile and possessed an outstanding cross-country ability.

Their usefulness was further enhanced by their ability to negotiate inland waterways under their own power.

The unitized body shell of the first prototype at the factory of Martini & Hüneke.

The Büssing-NAG version, also amphibious, was a 10×10 vehicle, tested extensively in Germany and Russia. These vehicles, all of which were multi-wheeled, proved to be too expensive under the given circumstances and were abandoned in favor of commercial 6×4 chassis.

These 6×4 chassis, available in large numbers from various manufacturers, were modified to accept an armored superstructure. Dual control was provided and the steering wheel inverted to allow for a better shaping of the armored body.

Schwerer Panzerspähwagen (6-Rad)
(Sd. Kfz. 232)

CREW	4		
COMBAT WEIGHT	5700 kp		
LENGTH	5570 mm		
WIDTH	1820 mm		
HEIGHT	2250 mm		
MAXIMUM SPEED	70 km/h		
MAXIMUM RANGE	300 km		
ARMAMENT	1 2 cm KwK 30		
	1 MG 13		
AMMUNITION	200		
	1300		
ARMOR	FRONT	14.5 mm	
	SIDE	8 mm	
	TOP	—	
	REAR	8 mm	
ENGINE	Daimler-Benz "M 09" 6 cyl inline, gasoline 68 HP		
TRANSMISSION	FORWARD 4×2	REVERSE 1×2	
FUEL CAPACITY	105 ltr.		
TRACK WIDTH	—		
MANUFACTURER	Daimler-Benz AG., Marienfelde		

This is the basic chassis of the Daimler-Benz version for the 6×4 armored car, which was also built by Büssing-NAG and Magirus.

During the maneuvers in 1932, these units appeared for the first time with actual armor and provided German reconnaissance units with a usable armored car.

The dual control is clearly indicated in this picture, as is the easy accessibility to the fighting compartment and the unique protection for the spare wheel.

This is the standard Sd. Kfz. 231, a vehicle equipped with a 2 cm gun in a 360° rotating turret.

While the standard unit is shown leading this small column, the following unit is a radio vehicle equipped with the overhead antenna, which characterized radio vehicles of this era.

This picture shows a heavy armored car with its turret in a 3 o'clock position. Clearly visible is the main armament and the coaxial machine gun. The spare tire arrangement was changed quite frequently.

Sd. Kfz. 232, the standard radio vehicle of the German Army, till the introduction of the 8-wheeled chassis.

This is the armored communication vehicle, called Sd. Kfz. 263, which was equipped with a rigid turret and a large, extendable radio mast. Small steel rollers, mounted on the frame between the front and rear wheels helped to improve cross-country ability.

Heavy German armored cars during the occupation of Prague in 1939. Vision slits and overhead protection for the reverse driver are clearly visible.

The dummy car development started, after unsuccessful attempts with truck chassis, with this Dixi automobile, a German version of the British Austin vehicle. Armor and armament were made out of plywood, wood and canvas.

An improved version of the dummy armored car was mounted on the commercial Adler chassis and was considered standard equipment during the development period, starting in 1932.

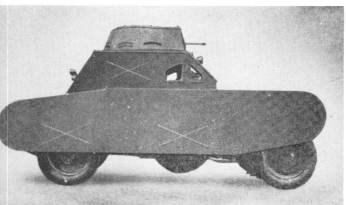

After the Adler chassis was phased out of production, an Opel chassis was used extensively for training purposes.

This picture shows details of the Opel "dummies" used during maneuvers in Germany before and during the war. The cross-country ability of these units left much to be desired.

They were supposed to be replaced starting in 1941 with the Volkswagen version, based upon the VW type 82 chassis. Only a limited number of these units were procured.

Some of the Adler chassis were provided with actual armor and used in limited numbers as light standard equipment for reconnaissance units. This vehicle is the Kfz. 13, a machine gun carrier.

Together with the 6-wheeled armored car, they outfitted various units until improved models were available starting in 1935.

Despite their limited ability in difficult terrain, experienced collected during their frequent use allowed German reconnaissance units to maintain a high level of training.

They saw action during the occupation of Czecho-slovakia in 1939, where they were used also for security purposes.

Because of restricted availability of improve vehicles, based on the 4×4 chassis, Adler un were actually used in combat during the campai against Poland in 1939.

The radio version carried no armament, but the usual foldable frame antenna. It accomodated a crew of three.

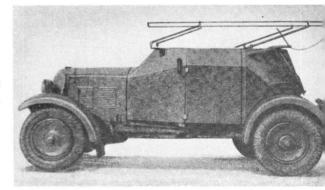

To replace it, a special version of the 4×4 heavy passenger car chassis was made available, to be fitted with armored superstructures. The engine was moved towards the rear of the chassis and the steering wheel, as usual, inclined.

ballistically well shaped hull, together with a rotating turret mounting a 2 cm gun and a coaxial machine gun, completed this very versatile vehicle.

Since no reverse driver could be accomodated, extensive preparations were made to allow these vehicles to withdraw quickly after contact with the enemy has been made. A battery of smoke candles mounted on the front of the unit facilitated such a maneuver.

The main armament of the vehicle could also be used for anti-aircraft purposes. Note the wire mesh cover, which normally closed the top of the open turret.

Leichter Panzerspähwagen (2 cm) (Sd.Kfz.222)

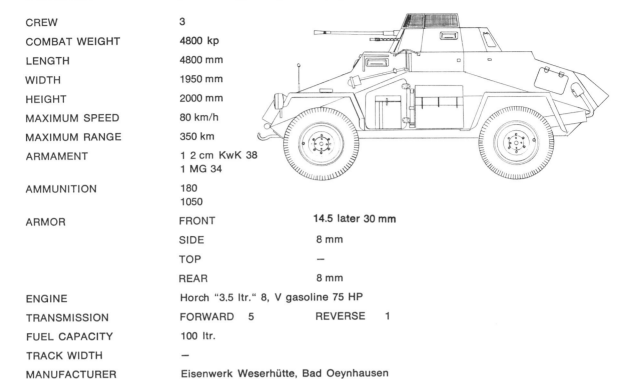

CREW	3
COMBAT WEIGHT	4800 kp
LENGTH	4800 mm
WIDTH	1950 mm
HEIGHT	2000 mm
MAXIMUM SPEED	80 km/h
MAXIMUM RANGE	350 km
ARMAMENT	1 2 cm KwK 38
	1 MG 34
AMMUNITION	180
	1050

ARMOR		
	FRONT	14.5 later 30 mm
	SIDE	8 mm
	TOP	—
	REAR	8 mm

ENGINE	Horch "3.5 ltr." 8, V gasoline 75 HP		
TRANSMISSION	FORWARD 5	REVERSE 1	
FUEL CAPACITY	100 ltr.		
TRACK WIDTH	—		
MANUFACTURER	Eisenwerk Weserhütte, Bad Oeynhausen		

An armored car unit being re-fueled during the campaign in Poland. Picture shows both basic versions of the standard light armored car.

They proved to be rather successful during the initial encounters and remained in troop service until the end of the war.

This is the standard Sd. Kfz. 222, the weapon carrier as it was produced in two versions from 1935 to 1943.

Sometimes the 2 cm gun was replaced by a 2.8 cm taper bore heavy anti-tank rifle to improve the anti-tank ability of reconnaissance units.

The light armored reconnaissance car, (Radio) Sd. Kfz. 223, had only one machine gun in a small turret and a collapsable frame antenna.

One version of another small armored radio car, Sd. Kfz. 260, carried no armament, but additional radio equipment.

Sd. Kfz. 261, also a small armored radio car, had, again, different radio equipment but no antenna.

Installation of the quick firing 2 cm gun and provisions for the coaxial machine gun are obvious, as are the hinged visors for the driver of the vehicle.

The basic vehicle was very compact in its dimensions and quite flexible, but its open turret made it vulnerable toward determined close range attacks.

Schwerer Panzerspähwagen (8-Rad)
(Sd. Kfz. 231) 2 cm KwK 30

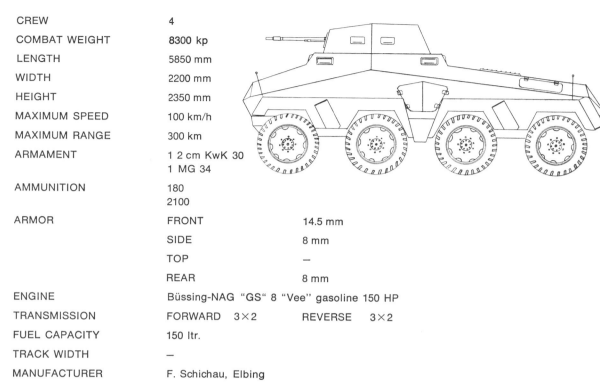

CREW	4	
COMBAT WEIGHT	8300 kp	
LENGTH	5850 mm	
WIDTH	2200 mm	
HEIGHT	2350 mm	
MAXIMUM SPEED	100 km/h	
MAXIMUM RANGE	300 km	
ARMAMENT	1 2 cm KwK 30	
	1 MG 34	
AMMUNITION	180	
	2100	
ARMOR	FRONT	14.5 mm
	SIDE	8 mm
	TOP	—
	REAR	8 mm
ENGINE	Büssing-NAG "GS" 8 "Vee" gasoline 150 HP	
TRANSMISSION	FORWARD 3×2	REVERSE 3×2
FUEL CAPACITY	150 ltr.	
TRACK WIDTH	—	
MANUFACTURER	F. Schichau, Elbing	

Based upon the experience with multi-wheeled vehicles in the late '20's the chassis type "GS" served as standard issue for German armored reconnaissance units for a substantial number of years.

Sd. Kfz. 231, as it appeared for the first time in 1935. A lightly armored vehicle of high mobility mounting a 2 cm gun and a coaxial machine gun in a rotating turret.

With a 4-man crew and capable of moving in either direction at the same speed, these units provided the backbone for most armored reconnaissance units.

Front view of the unit shows a ballistically well designed superstructure. The vehicle shown here is of late issue.

Crew entering the vehicle. Various means of accessibility were provided.

A vehicle of later issue on a reconnaissance mission. Hidden if possible from the enemy, it maintained vital communication between armored formations. Note steel helmets of crew mounted on the outside of the unit.

One of the vehicles captured in Africa, where it proved itself to be quite adequate for all tasks. Vehicles used in North Africa were delivered with additional air filters, and different reduction ratios for the cooling fans.

A later issue vehicle with frame antenna. Through an ingenius arrangement, the turret could still be fully rotated.

Armored car crew receiving an order for further employment. The mounting and arrangement for the main armament is clearly visible.

Because of its inadequate armor protection, most of the units received additional armor shields hinged upon the front of the vehicles. The limited payload capacity of the chassis, however, did not allow for a basic increase in armor strength.

Highly mobile, these units were not obliged to use roads but stayed quite frequently off the beaten path. The unit above is shown on a reconnaissance mission in Yugoslavia.

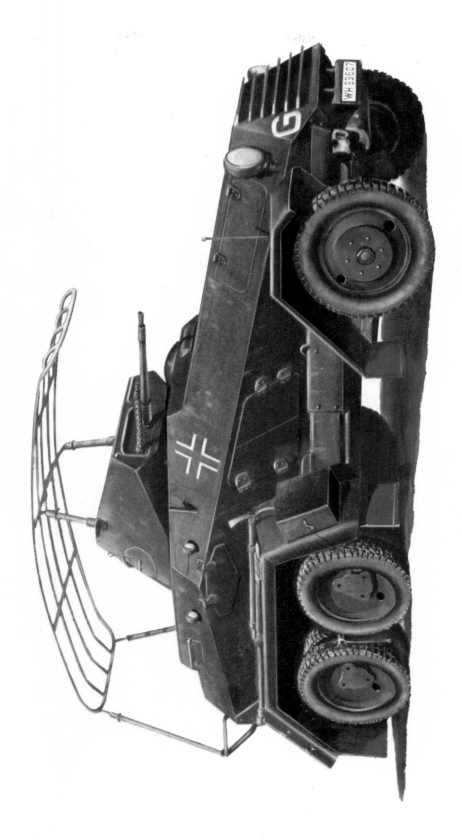

PANZERSPÄHWAGEN (Sd. Kfz. 232) (Funk)

Uwe Feist

PANZERSPÄHWAGEN (Sd. Kfz. 231)

PANZERSPÄHWAGEN (Sd. Kfz. 234/2) "PUMA"

The cumbersome and very obvious frame antenna was later on replaced by a regular poletype one, which made communication vehicles not as easy a target as their predecessors.

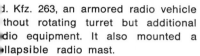

d. Kfz. 263, an armored radio vehicle thout rotating turret but additional dio equipment. It also mounted a llapsible radio mast.

As a support vehicle for armored reconnaissance units, this Sd. Kfz. 233 mounted a 75 mm tank gun in limited traverse. Note smoke candles attached to the front fenders of the unit.

They were protected against adverse weather only by means of a canvas top, since the fighting compartment was left open to better accommodate the crew.

A support vehicle in North Africa displaying the installation of the main armament, and the sighting device for the gunner and commander.

A front view of the same vehicle shows the stowage of tools and various other components. Smoke candles are evident on both front fenders.

The gun, which used to be the main armament of the Panzer IV, served its purpose well in providing necessary fire support during reconnaissance missions.

The new 234 series of armored cars was easily recognizable on the larger diameter wheels.

While the suspension was still the same as on its predecessor, it was propelled now by an air-cooled 210 hp Tatra diesel engine.

The 2 cm turret was open but protected by a wire mesh roof, which allowed for easy accessibility to the turret. The diesel engine gave the unit a range of almost 600 miles.

Panzerspähwagen "Puma" (Sd. Kfz. 234/2)
(5 cm) KwK 39/1 L/60

CREW	4		
COMBAT WEIGHT	11740 kp		
LENGTH	6800 mm		
WIDTH	2330 mm		
HEIGHT	2380 mm		
MAXIMUM SPEED	90 km/h		
MAXIMUM RANGE	1000 km		
ARMAMENT	1 5 cm KwK 39/1 L/60		
	1 MG 42		
AMMUNITION	55		
	2850		
ARMOR	FRONT	30 mm	
	SIDE	8 mm	
	TOP	—	
	REAR	10 mm	
ENGINE	Tatra "111" 12, V diesel 210 HP		
TRANSMISSION	FORWARD 3×2	REVERSE	3×2
FUEL CAPACITY	360 ltr.		
TRACK WIDTH	—		
MANUFACTURER	Büssing-NAG, Leipzig		

The turret for this Sd. Kfz. 234/2 was originally developed for a full-tracked reconnaissance vehicle. It mounted the 5 cm L/60 gun, which used to be the main armament for the Panzer III.

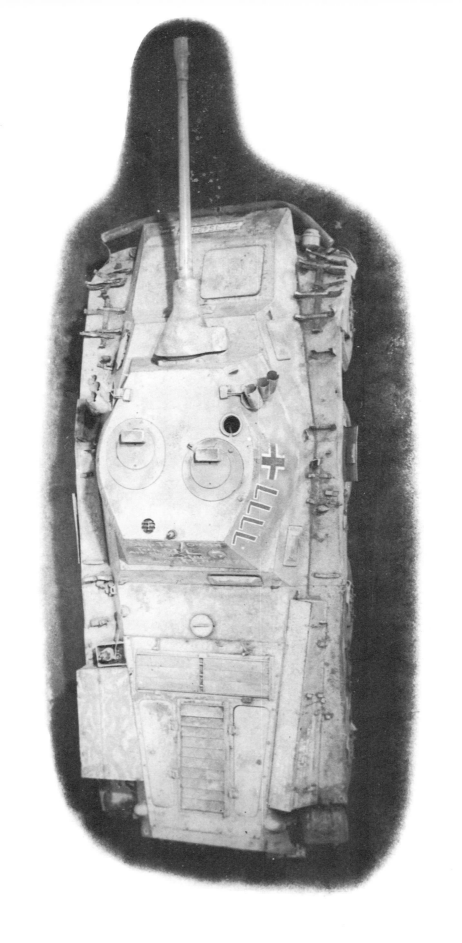

Ballistically well formed, this unit was without a doubt one of the most advanced armored cars of the second World War.

Notice the "Saukopfblende" on the main armament, together with a muzzle brake, which was absent on the Panzer III. Smoke candles are now housed in containers mounted on the turret.

The radio version of the car had the same armament but additional radio equipment and the pole antenna already available for the late version of the Sd. Kfz. 232.

The support version of this series was again equipped with the short-barreled 75 mm gun.

The exhaust configuration of the 12 cylinder Diesel engine is shown on this picture. The same engine was standard equipment for the 6½ ton German Army truck.

The fighting compartment was open and easily accessible. The unit was thus most vulnerable toward close range attacks.

To provide more punch for reconnaissance units, an attempt was made to mount the 75 mm Pak 40 L/48. Only a limited number of these units saw troop service.

This vehicle carried the nomenclature Sd. Kfz. 247 and was based upon the 6×4 Krupp truck chassis. It was mainly intended for high-ranking staff officers.

It was replaced by the standard chassis for the heavy passenger car, which had its engine mounted in the front. It was lightly armored only and served as a command car for various purposes.

For export purposes, the standard Krupp 6×4 light truck chassis was fitted with armored superstructures and some of them had been sold to the Dutch East Indies.

The amphibious "turtle" series also incorporated an armored ammunition carrier. Only prototypes were built.

The armored car version of the "turtle" appeared with various armaments. It was amphibious but so lightly armored that its basic purpose could not be fulfilled. It never went into mass production.

The Saurer wheel cum-track Sd. Kfz. 254 was issued only at the beginning of the war. It soon proved mechanically unreliable and was not re-procured.

It was mainly used as an armored observation vehicle for artillery units. A total of only 140 of these units were in use.

PANZERSPÄHWAGEN (Sd. Kfz. 231)   License No. WL 45180

AN *ARMOR* SERIES SPECIAL

VOL. 6

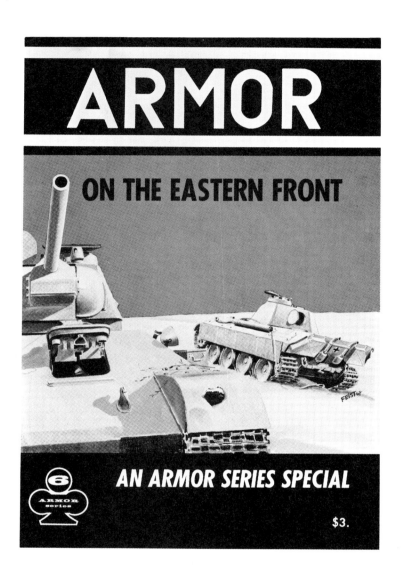

ARMOR

ON THE EASTERN FRONT

AN ARMOR SERIES SPECIAL

6

ARMOR series

$3.

ARMOR ON THE EASTERN FRONT

52 pages   4 pages of color   110 photos and drawings $3.00

Former Tank Commander and noted German armor authority Walter Spielberger and talented artist Uwe Feist again team up....this time to present Volume 6 in the Armor Series. Varying from the usual series format of featuring only one tank-type per book, this Armor Series Special presents both the German and Russian tank equipment used in the Eastern Campaign between 1941 and 1945.